Grey Rabbit and the Circus

The Little Grey Rabbit Library

Grey Rabbit and
the Circus

Alison Uttley

pictures by Margaret Tempest

Collins

William Collins Sons & Co Ltd
London · Glasgow · Sydney · Auckland
Toronto · Johannesburg

First published 1961
© text The Alison Uttley Literary Property Trust 1987
© illustrations The Estate of Margaret Tempest 1987
© this arrangement William Collins Sons & Co Ltd 1987
Third impression 1988
Cover decoration by Fiona Owen
Decorated capital by Mary Cooper
Alison Uttley's original story has been abridged for this book.
Uttley, Alison
Little Grey Rabbit and the circus. —
Rev. ed. — (Little Grey Rabbit books)
I. Title   II. Tempest, Margaret
III. Series
823'.912 [J] PZ10.3

ISBN 0-00-194215-8

Typeset by Columns of Reading
Made and printed in Great Britain by
William Collins Sons and Co Ltd, Glasgow

FOREWORD

Of course you must understand that Grey Rabbit's home had no electric light or gas, and even the candles were made from pith of rushes dipped in wax from the wild bees' nests, which Squirrel found. Water there was in plenty, but it did not come from a tap. It flowed from a spring outside, which rose up from the ground and went to a brook. Grey Rabbit cooked on a fire, but it was a wood fire, there was no coal in that part of the country. Tea did not come from India, but from a little herb known very well to country people, who once dried it and used it in their cottage homes. Bread was baked from wheat ears, ground fine, and Hare and Grey Rabbit gleaned in the cornfields to get the wheat.

The doormats were plaited rushes, like country-made mats, and cushions were stuffed with wool gathered from the hedges where sheep pushed through the thorns. As for the looking-glass, Grey Rabbit found the glass, dropped from a lady's handbag, and Mole made a frame for it. Usually the animals gazed at themselves in the still pools as so many country children have done. The country ways of Grey Rabbit were the country ways known to the author.

L ittle Grey Rabbit looked out of the kitchen door early one morning, to welcome the sun and nod to the trees. The sun was in the sky and the trees were in the wood, but the sun was too busy looking at something in the field to notice Grey Rabbit. So Grey Rabbit looked too.

"It wasn't there last night. Has it grown?" she asked.

It was exactly like a large red-and-white striped mushroom.

"A mushroom or a toadstool. They come up quickly in the night," she thought.

"Hare! Squirrel!" she called. "Wake up and come and see."

Hare and Squirrel tumbled out of their beds and nearly fell downstairs in their hurry.

"It's a 'nor-mous toadstool, red as a poppy," said Hare.

"It's an umbrella," said Squirrel. "It's like my parasol I lost in the river."

"We'll get dressed and go and look at it before it fades away," said Hare. "Don't go without us, Grey Rabbit."

They scampered up to their rooms, threw on some clothes and hurried back.

"Come along, follow me," cried Hare, boldly leading the way.

They hurried through the fields, but when they approached the toadstool they went slowly, for they could see what it was. It was a tent, made of gossamer-silk, and the wind caused it to billow and sway. The folds of the tent opened and a Black Hare stepped out. He was a handsome fellow, with laughing eyes and jigging step.

He carried a bunch of ivy leaves, and a hazel stick with some wild flowers fastened to the top.

"Good morning, Hare, Squirrel and Little Grey Rabbit," said he, bowing and leaping towards the three. He offered his green stick to Grey Rabbit.

"We have pitched our tent in your field, Grey Rabbit, and we will pay you a day's rent of a pinch of fern seed. Here is a free pass to our circus."

Grey Rabbit took the hazel stick, but she was rather nervous of this prancing Hare.

"Circus, Sir Hare?" she stammered.

"I am the leader of our circus. We have travelled the land, we have acted in meadow and copse, on heath and common, in bog and on moorland."

"We have even danced before Kings and Queens," said the Black Hare, proudly.

"Kings and Queens?" echoed Grey Rabbit.

"Well, King-fishers and Queen Bees," explained the Black Hare.

"King-cups and Queen-of-the-meadows," added Squirrel.

"King of Hearts and Queen of Spades," said Hare, who had played Snap with the Fox.

"Yes, all those Kings and Queens," said the Black Hare. "And now we have come to your home to show you our dances and tricks."

"Oh! Oh! Thank you," cried Squirrel, Hare and Grey Rabbit. "This is a treat in a quiet place where we never hear a song except that of the blackbird and throstle and nightingale, and we never see any magic except Wise Owl's tricks," said Hare.

"Do you know Wise Owl?" asked Grey Rabbit.

"I've heard of him. I shall invite him to our performance," said the Black Hare. "But I must hurry away. I have these ivy notes to deliver to all the cottages of the woods and fields."

"Don't forget to call at Moldy Warp's hill," shouted Hare. "You might miss it."

"And at Water-rat's, down by the river," added Squirrel.

"And please invite Mr and Mrs Rat and their baby," said little Grey Rabbit. "Nobody asks them to anything."

"But don't invite the Weasels," said Squirrel and Hare.

The Black Hare promised he would not call on the Weasels, and away he went, fairly galloping over the field, so that Hare stared after him with envy.

"There's writing on this ivy-leaf," said Grey Rabbit, "but I cannot read it. Can you, Fuzzypeg?"

Fuzzypeg, who had come to visit his friends, held the letter close to his nose.

"It says, 'Dances, Tricks, Clowns'."

They all ran indoors and made the breakfast, talking excitedly about the circus.

Hare burned the toast, and Squirrel dropped the new-laid egg on the floor and Grey Rabbit made the tea without putting any tea in the pot. Even Fuzzypeg caught his spikes on the table-cloth and dragged it off the table.

Then Old Hedgehog came to the door with the milk.

"Milk-o! Milk-o!" he cried. "Have you seen it? There's a travelling show with a tent outside in the field. Have you seen the sight, Miss Grey Rabbit and Miss Squirrel?"

Then he spied little Fuzzypeg sitting wrapped up in the tablecloth trying to disentangle his prickles.

"There you are, Fuzzypeg! Up to mischief! Your mother is looking for you," said he severely; but his eyes brightened with joy as he looked at the little Hedgehog.

"We know all about the tent," said Hare, in a lordly way. "There's the Black Hare and his circus, and the Seven Clowns."

"Seven!" cried Hedgehog. "Seven, same as the stars in the Great Bear?"

"What are clowns?" asked Squirrel.

"Animals like me and you," piped Fuzzypeg.

"We are going to see them this afternoon," said Grey Rabbit, happily.

"Oh my!" Hedgehog blinked his eyes and rattled his quills and stamped his little feet in

20

a clog dance. "What a stir in our countryside! What a to-do in the fields! Nay, I've never heard tell of such a thing since the cow jumped over the moon."

"You must bring Mrs Hedgehog," said Hare.

"She will bring me," said Old Hedgehog. "Fuzzypeg's here all ready to go along of you."

Throughout the morning many little animals came peeping through the bushes, creeping along the paths in the thick grass, peering at the red-and-white tent among the buttercups.

Some rabbits brought their dinners and sat waiting for the performance to begin. A family of field mice carried a hamper of food and sat on it. Squirrels swung from the trees and frogs hopped in the wet ditches. All wanted to be in time.

The Speckledy Hen came clucking up. Water-rat appeared in his best velvet coat, and his housekeeper Mrs Webster brought a few cakes for the hungry ones.

Squirrel, Hare and little Grey Rabbit in their best clothes joined the gathering. The Rat with his wife and baby stood in the distance, waiting by the ferny hollow. Wise Owl sat sleepily yawning in a tree near the tent.

At last the tent door opened.

The Black Hare stepped out.

"Walk up! Come closer!" he called.

The animals came near. They squatted on the sloping bank by the tent, where they could get a good view.

"My friends," said the Black Hare, "may I present the artistes in my circus?"

He drew back the folds of the tent and from its shadows came a magnificent Cock with a long sweeping tail.

"That's our Cockadoodle, who ran away from the farm," whispered the Speckledy Hen.

Next came a rabbit, brushed and shining, with a round little face and twitching ears. She bent her pretty head and made a curtsey to the audience.

"This is Snow-White," said the Black Hare, "and here are the seven clowns."

Seven fat little dormice rolled on the grass
and twisted themselves into knots as they
tumbled about like small brown clowns.

The snow rabbit stood there in her flower-
petal skirt, and then she danced.

"Is she real?" asked Fuzzypeg.

The Black Hare turned to him. "You may
well ask, my little Hedgehog," said he. "She
is the prettiest rabbit in the world. She won a
prize at the County Show, but she was
unhappy in her hutch. She was a
prisoner like all of us – for I was a
captive, too. We escaped, then
the dormice joined us and the
Cock flew to us from the farm.

"Here we are to amuse you. We sing our songs and perform our tricks and we live in a tent which was woven for us by the gossamer spiders."

He bowed, and everyone cheered and stamped so that there was a noise like the wind, with soft feet drumming and little bodies rustling. The Fox heard it, but when he came towards the circle of animals there was an invisible barrier which no savage creature could get through. It had been made by the Black Hare who had spilled fern seed all around to protect the circus.

"The Cock will open with a song," said the Black Hare. And the Cock stepped forward.

> "Cock-a-doodle-doo.
> We've brought our play to you.
> We sing and dance
> And lightly prance
> To wish you how-d'ye-do."

His shrill cock-a-doodle carried over the fields to the farmyard.

"Listen! I wish he would come back," said the Hens.

Next the Black Hare leapt through a hoop which the Cock held and all the little dormice leapt after him. He climbed a ladder and balanced on the top rung. He walked along a tight-rope of rushes. He tumbled head over heels on the grass and the dormice rolled after him.

Little Grey Rabbit sat with her eyes wide open, longing to be a beautiful dancing rabbit in a flower-petal dress. She looked at her own little grey dress, and she sighed.

Hare was gazing at the Black Hare, wishing he could be like him. Fuzzypeg laughed at the dormice, rolling about like clowns all the time. He knew he could roll, but he couldn't spin through the grass like those little balls. Squirrel was whispering to the Speckledy Hen.

"Yes, dear Speckledy Hen. He is a beautiful Cock. I wish he would return to your farmyard."

"Yes, dear Squirrel, I do wish he would," sighed the Speckledy Hen.

"Can anyone lend me a watch?" asked the Black Hare, stepping among the animals with an air of importance. Each one shuffled and felt in his pocket. Nobody had a watch except Hare.

"I'll lend you mine," said Hare, proudly holding up his turnip watch.

The Black Hare took it in his paw, and held it dangling by its chain. "Twelve o'clock," said the Black Hare, then: "Presto. Pass!" he added, and at the magical words the watch disappeared.

It was nowhere. It had completely gone. Poor Hare looked very sad, and Grey Rabbit had to comfort him.

"What is that on top of yonder beech tree?" asked the Black Hare, and they all looked skywards.

"Come down from yonder tree! Come along here!" he commanded. Then he added: "Will you now feel in your pocket, Mister Hare?"

Hare put his hand in his pocket and there was the turnip watch. It said 1 o'clock.

"I can do better than that," hooted Wise Owl. "I can make the watch disappear and never come back."

"Not today, sir. Not today," said the Black Hare, hurriedly, and Wise Owl shrugged his shoulders.

The Black Hare then produced yards of daisy chains from Grey Rabbit's apron-pocket, and a flock of butterflies from Squirrel's dress.

He whistled and a swallow-tail flew from Fuzzypeg's smock, and a red admiral from Mrs Hedgehog's umbrella.

In the Water-rat's frills a bumble-bee played a tune.

Marvellous! Wonderful! Everyone was astonished at the conjuring tricks.

"Thank you, dear friends, for your patronage," said the Black Hare.

"Three cheers for the Black Hare, the Snow Rabbit, the Cock and the Dormice," said Mole, and everyone waved and cried, "Hurrah!"

It was nearly dusk when some of them reached home. The tent was closed and all was quiet.

In the early morning Squirrel looked out of her window, and saw an empty field. Quickly she got up and dressed. She packed a little bag with her nightgown and her teasel brush, and slipped quietly downstairs and ran across the common following the trail of the circus.

Hare also looked out of his window. He, too, dressed and followed the travelling show, with his watch and his flute.

Then Grey Rabbit awoke and looked out. She dressed and ran downstairs. She seized her cloak and put on her goloshes, and followed the track in the dewy field.

When she got to the top of the hill she could see far away the little red-and-white tent carried by the Black Hare, while the White Rabbit and the Dormice trotted behind. Then she saw Hare, lolloping along and Squirrel racing after.

"We are all running away from home," she said. "We are all running away. Oh! how foolish we are."

The Cock leaned out from a tree and spoke to her.

"I am not running away, Grey Rabbit. I am going back to the farm, to see dear old Speckledy Hen again. They will have to carry on without me."

"Oh, I am glad you are going back to Speckledy Hen," said Grey Rabbit.

"I can see Squirrel and Hare over there. They are turning round. They are coming home," continued the Cock.

Sure enough Hare and Squirrel caught up with them before they got home, and they had a merry breakfast together.

"Good-bye, Grey Rabbit," called the Cock as he set off to the farmyard. "Good-bye. I shall see you again soon."

"I nearly joined that circus," said Hare.

"So did I," said Squirrel.

"We all nearly ran away," laughed Grey Rabbit. "But home is best."